Helen Orme taught for many years before giving up teaching to write full-time. At the last count she had written over 70 books.

She writes both fiction and non-fiction, but at present is concentrating on fiction for older readers.

Helen also runs writing workshops for children and courses for teachers in both primary and secondary schools.

Open Wide

by

Helen Orme

Ransom

Open Wide
by Helen Orme
Illustrated by Chris Askham

Published by Ransom Publishing Ltd.
Radley House, 8 St. Cross Road, Winchester, Hampshire SO23 9HX, UK
www.ransom.co.uk

ISBN   978 184167 154 3
First published in 2013
Copyright © 2013 Ransom Publishing Ltd.

Illustrations copyright © 2013 Chris Askham

Siti Musa

Wall · Photos · Friends

Hi! I'm Siti Musa.

Siti is a Swahili (African) name meaning 'Lady'.

I'm the oldest in my family. I have two brothers, Daudi and Hanif, and a kid sister Afia.

My dad is a deputy head at our school, which can be bad news sometimes!

My mum is a social worker.

Lu Clarke

Wall · Photos · Friends

I'm Lu Clarke and I'm an only child. My dad is a businessman – he has an IT office in the town centre. My mum, who is Chinese, works in a bank.

My mum's parents (Po-po and Gong-gong – our name for grandparents) live by the sea. They used to have a Chinese restaurant and my mum worked there when she was younger. My other grandparents live close to us.

My parents want the best for me – but they don't always ask me what *I* want.

Kelly Jonson

Wall · Photos · Friends

I'm Kelly Jonson.

My mum is a single parent. She works as a solicitor. I've got an older brother, Jamie. His girlfriend is Susie.

My parents split when I was very young, and Dad remarried. We don't have any contact with Dad and his new family.

I really want to be a writer – oh, and I fancy Gary! I've decided that I want to be a vegetarian.

Rachel Phillips

Wall · Photos · Friends

I'm Rachel Phillips.

My parents split about 4 years ago. Dad runs a small printing business, and Mum is office manager at our school.

I live with Mum and spend weekends with Dad. His new wife is Janine. They have two young children, a boy and a new baby girl. It's O.K. visiting them, but I'd rather be with Mum.

My older brother Wil is at sixth-form college.

Donna Mills

Wall · Photos · Friends

I'm Donna Mills.

My dad's a bus driver and my mum works in a shop.

I have two older sisters, Marie and Briony. Marie's friend Susie is Kelly's brother's girlfriend.

My brother, Michael, is the youngest.

I love animals and going swimming.

There isn't much spare cash in our family – which makes things hard sometimes.

Chapter 1

Siti and Donna went to call for Lu at her house.

Lu opened the door. She had already got her coat and bag.

'Come on,' she said. 'Let's get out of here.'

She started off down the garden path.

'Hey, what's the matter?' asked Siti.

'Have you had a row?' said Donna.

Lu shook her head. 'No.'

Donna looked at Siti. Lu was rushing on ahead.

'She's just in a mood,' Donna whispered. 'Leave her alone. She'll get over it soon.'

But, whatever it was, she didn't get over it.

* * * * *

At school, Kelly and Rachel tried to talk to her too, but she wouldn't say much. She just sat at her desk and kept shaking her head.

When it got to break-time they crowded round.

'What's wrong?'

'You can tell us.'

'We might be able to help.'

But Lu put her head in her hands. 'You can't help. Go away.'

* * * * *

The next lesson was P. E. Lu looked awful.

'I don't want to do it,' she said.

Siti went over to Mrs Carter to tell her. Mrs Carter looked at Lu.

'Go to the school office,' she said to Lu.
'They'll ring your mum and you can go
home.'

Chapter
2

At the end of morning lessons they went to the cloakroom. Lu was there. She still looked awful and she had been crying.

'Didn't they send you home?' asked Kelly.

'I didn't go to the office,' Lu said. 'I don't want to go home.'

'What's wrong?' said Rachel.

'I've got toothache,' wailed Lu.

'Did you tell your mum?' asked Donna.

'She'll make me go to the dentist. I *hate* the dentist. She's a horrible old woman.'

'No she's not,' said Kelly. 'I have the same dentist and she's really nice. Friendly, and chatty and cheerful.'

'That's the trouble,' sniffed Lu. 'I can't stand it when she tries to make you talk when she's stuffing things in your mouth.'

Siti couldn't help it: she laughed.

'It's not funny.' Lu glared at Siti.

'What are you going to do then?' asked Rachel.

'Nothing!'

'Try stuffing tissues in your mouth,' suggested Kelly. 'Make a sort of cushion for your tooth.'

Lu got a tissue and put it in her mouth. It was all right for a couple of minutes, then she spat out a horrible soggy, stringy mess.

'Yuck,' she said. 'I think I'm going to be sick.'

Chapter
3

'You need something hot on it,' said Rachel.

'No, you need ice,' said Kelly.

'This is getting silly,' said Siti. 'There's nothing we can do. Go to the office and see if you can go home.'

'We'll take you, this time,' added Donna. 'You've got to do something.'

* * * * *

Next day was Saturday and they met at Siti's house. Lu seemed a bit happier.

'What did your mum say?'

'I've got to go to the dentist, but I can't go until next week. It might get better by then.'

'Is it better now?' said Rachel.

Lu took a packet out of her pocket. 'Mum gave me some painkillers and I've got the rest of the packet.'

'You can't keep taking those!' said Kelly.
'Too many is bad for you.'

'Don't tell me what to do,' snapped Lu.
'You're not the one with toothache.'

'I know,' said Siti. 'Mum's got some stuff for Afia. You could try that.'

She went to the bathroom and got a bottle of pink stuff. Lu put a spoonful in her mouth and spat it out again.

'It's horrible! How can you feed that to your little sister?'

'Well she likes it.'

'I don't! I'd rather take these.'

Kelly grabbed the pill packet. 'You can't have any more.'

'But it's hurting again,' Lu wailed.

Chapter
4

'I know,' said Donna. 'Let's look on the Internet for ideas.'

They went up to Siti's room and switched on her computer. Soon they had a page of websites to search.

The girls were enjoying themselves, but Lu wasn't amused.

'Find something sensible,' she said.

'Here's one,' said Kelly. 'Tea-tree oil.'

'We've got that,' said Siti, 'but I think it's hand wash!'

'What about this?' asked Donna, pointing to the screen. 'Mustard oil and turmeric!'

'What's turmeric?' asked Rachel.

'It's a spice,' said Lu. 'But I'm not putting that in my mouth.'

In the end Lu got fed up and went home. They didn't see her again until Monday morning.

* * * * *

'Look,' said Siti, waving a sheet of paper at her friends. 'I've found loads more ideas.'
She gave the sheet to Donna, who read it out loud.

'Get a dead mouse and put it on your tooth! Get a tooth from a dead body and wear it round your neck.'

Lu tried to grab the sheet, but Donna passed it over to Kelly.

'Wear a magpie's beak round your neck. Oh, here's one you might like: put a clove of garlic in your ear.'

Chapter
5

At last Lu grabbed the paper. She opened her bag and stuffed it inside.

'It's not funny!' she said, but by now even she was laughing.

She hadn't noticed that something had fallen out of her bag. She went off for her first lesson.

Siti picked up the thing that had fallen. It was a letter, addressed to Mrs Gray, their form tutor.

Siti handed it to Mrs Gray. 'I think this is from Lu,' she said. 'She forgot to give it to you.'

* * * * *

After lunch they were back in the form room.

'Are you still here?' said Mrs Gray, looking at Lu. 'You'd better go straight away or you will be late for the dentist.'

Lu looked at Siti. 'How did she know?' she whispered.

'Was that your letter? You dropped it, so
I handed it in.'

Lu decided she had no choice now and went off.

* * * * *

Later that afternoon, when Lu got back to school, she was looking very happy.

'Better now?' asked Siti.

'Much better. It's been filled, it doesn't hurt and I'm going back next week.'

'Why are you so happy then?' asked Kelly. 'You hate the dentist.'

'Not any more. That woman left and there's a new one.

'And he's gorgeous!'

Siti's Sisters
The early years

– one year on:
the Sisters
are older

Helen Orme
Brother Bother
Illustrated by Cathy Brett

Helen Orme
Horsing Around
Illustrated by Cathy Brett

Helen Orme
New Man
Illustrated by Cathy Brett

Helen Orme
Who's Who
Illustrated by Cathy Brett

Helen Orme
Wet!
Illustrated by Cathy Brett

Helen Orme
Illustrated by Cathy Brett

– another year on:
The Sisters have grown up (well, nearly ...)

Helen Orme
Party Time
Illustrated by Chris Askham

Helen Orme
She's My Friend Now
Illustrated by Chris Askham

Helen Orme
Leave Her Alone
Illustrated by Chris Askham

Helen Orme
Secrets
Illustrated by Chris Askham

Helen Orme
Sleepover
Illustrated by Chris Askham

Helen Orme
Don't Do It!
Illustrated by Chris Askham